CONSUMER GUIDE®



# GAS SAVERS GUIDE

Louis Weber, President
Publications International, Ltd.
3841 West Oakton Street
Skokie, Illinois 60076


Manufactured in the United States of America
1 2 3 4 5 6 7 8 9 10

Cover Design: Frank E. Peiler
Cartoons: David Harbaugh

# CONTENTS

# INTRODUCTION:

# CUTTING FUEL EXPENSES

If you're worried about not being able to buy gasoline when you need it, as well as about the increasing price of gas, this book is for you. The price of gasoline is already well over a dollar a gallon, so owning a car is more of a hardship than ever before. Cut down on your use of fuel and you'll spend less money on your car. This book shows you how to live with less gasoline.

Saving gas and money is really a lot easier than you might think. Most of us learned to drive the way we do without much regard for getting the most miles out of a gallon of gas. The cars we dreamed about, and later purchased, were always longer, lower, wider, more powerful, and thirstier than last year's models. When we worried about car maintenance, it was usually because the car didn't accelerate quickly enough—not because the mileage was low. Sometimes we tried to get even more performance from our cars by bolting on extra carburetors, dual exhaust systems, headers, and special camshafts.

America's love affair with the automobile bloomed in the era of cheap gas. But like nickel pop and high-button shoes, those days are gone for good. Yet most of us still depend on our cars to get to work, for shopping—maybe even for our living. If economic necessity means most of us must keep on driving, how can we afford to continue doing so?

Tests show that almost every driver can substantially improve his fuel economy, and not just by eliminating unnecessary trips. One study conducted by the American Automobile Association in Michigan showed that careless driving can result in a 44 percent fuel loss compared with driving techniques that help conserve gasoline. In fact, the habits of the driver have a larger impact on fuel consumption than either an untuned engine or the indiscriminate use of an air conditioner. Use of an air conditioner causes a 10 percent fuel economy loss, and a badly tuned engine results in a loss of about 7 percent.

Poor driving habits in the Michigan test included "jack rabbit" starts, rapid stops, weaving in and out of traffic, and rapid acceleration to the point of having to spike the brakes to avoid ramming the car ahead. Traveling in afternoon traffic, the test drivers achieved over 14 mpg using careful driving techniques and just about 8 mpg driving carelessly. Similar results occurred in another test performed in rush-hour conditions.

The advantage of adopting more economical driving habits is that, once acquired, the habits stick with you and need only a little brushing up from time to time. Improve your mileage by 10 percent, and you save $80 to $100 a year, depending on the type of car you drive and how far you drive.

How much will these tips actually save you in gasoline and money? That's difficult to figure precisely. Many drivers can achieve a cash savings of 25 percent over a period of time. If you drive a car like the Chevrolet Caprice, that would mean an extra $150 in your pocket. Even drivers of the Volkswagen Rabbit diesel, the economy champion, can achieve savings of $55 a year, or more. Of course, by combining trips, taking a bus, or by driving a more economical car than the one you now use, savings will not show up as actual mpg improvements. That's why the total annual fuel cost figure is important when figuring your actual driving costs. By moving closer to work or joining a car pool, you might not improve your car's economy, but you would spend fewer dollars for gas overall.

For the most part, driving efficiently requires no special sacrifice or change in life style. You can still enjoy the freedom of driving your car, plus the bonus of saving gas, money, and worry.

# PART ONE:

# DRIVING EFFICIENTLY

Poor driving habits that have been developed over a lifetime can be difficult to break, but the rising price of gasoline has become a real incentive for most people to *do something.* For virtually all drivers, the solution is simple: Replace the poor habits with good ones. The tips presented in this section will help you do just that so you can achieve two sensible goals: get optimal performance out of your car, and get the most miles per dollar.

Driving economically might require some sacrifices, but not as many as you think. For example, using the car's ventilation system to circulate cool, fresh air can be just as comfortable as switching on the air-conditioning—and far more economical.

One good way to approach the art of driving economically is to set a goal for yourself. If, for instance, you would like to improve your car's fuel economy by 25 percent, and if you're a typical driver, only a few changes in your driving habits will let you accomplish this goal. Just by maintaining a steady speed wherever you drive, you may be able to increase your mileage considerably. Before long, you'll find that the challenge of becoming a better driver can be fun.

The gas-saving and money-saving ideas in this section are easy to use. They'll start you on the road to saving money immediately. They will also serve as a good measure of your car's mechanical condition. Should you, despite your best efforts, find your car still suffers from poor fuel economy, you'll know that something is wrong. Perhaps your car needs a tune-up; perhaps a filter is clogged. Things that rob your car of efficiency and performance are recognizable early if you are an observant, fuel-conscious driver. And you can have the trouble repaired before you pour too much gas down the drain.

If you're among those who are fed up with fuel bills, put these tips to work right away. If you have a good idea of what your car's weekly fuel consumption is, and you implement these gas-saving suggestions immediately, you'll begin to notice a big change the first week. The good driving habits you've acquired will remain with you and serve as fuel-conservation aids for the rest of your driving life.

**Plan your short trips.**
Instead of making a half dozen short trips a day, plan ahead so that the number can be cut to one or two. You'll save a lot of gas, plus wear and tear on your car, by combining these trips or sharing rides with your neighbors. In the winter when temperatures are low and roadways are slippery, such short jaunts are the toughest kind of driving for your car and your fuel economy. Stop-and-go driving with a partially warmed-up engine is expensive. Set up a driving schedule and follow it.

*"I'm leaving the car home once a week so you can fill it with gas"*

**Plan your route.**
The shortest (and therefore the most economical) distance between two points isn't always a straight line. If you drive one particular route each day, experiment with alternatives. Time yourself, consider how many stoplights or traffic jams you must wait for along each route, and measure the distance with your odometer. One route might take you a few blocks out of your way but allow you to bypass a bottleneck. Try routes that take you to your destination at highway speeds rather than city speeds—the difference in mileage could be significant.

**Get to know the school zones.**
They mean a slowdown to an uneconomical 15 mph—or even worse, a complete stop. Avoid routes that take you through a school zone during school hours.

**Pay attention to radio reports.**
Radio stations in most big cities broadcast rush-hour traffic reports. Make a practice of checking for reports of tie-ups on your route as soon as you leave the house or work each day. They are especially valuable in inclement weather when most of the worst tie-ups occur. Take an alternate route or delay your departure to avoid the trouble spots.

**Clean out your trunk.**
There are some things you'll always want to carry in the trunk, such as a small set of tools for emergencies, perhaps an extra can of oil, etc. But there are lots of other things you don't have to carry. Tire chains, snow tires, sandbags, golf clubs, and bowling balls are heavy. And a heavy car uses more gasoline than a light car does.

**Distribute weight evenly.**
Don't pack all the extra weight you have to carry in the trunk. The weight will lift the front end and hamper the car's carefully formulated aerodynamics. In front-drive cars, a front axle lightened in this way reduces drive traction, causes wheel slip, wastes gas.

**Load your car-top carrier wisely.**
Think about aerodynamics as you position cargo on your roof rack. Try to arrange the items to minimize the frontal area of the load. A roof rack loaded with a few suitcases or boxes can decrease highway mileage by as much as 0.5 to 1 mpg.

**Dress properly.**
In summer, dress in light, cool clothes so you won't need to turn on the air conditioner or open all the windows. Why keep your jacket on and start up the AC to cool off?

**Use the warm car.**
If you have two cars in your family, use the one that is already warmed up instead of the cold one and you'll minimize the choke-on time that's normally needed to get a car running most efficiently. Eliminating the choke time can save up to 5 mpg in the first mile or two of driving. This is especially beneficial on cold days when the engine takes a long time to warm up.

**Don't turn the key till you're ready to go.**
Get yourself ready to drive before starting the engine. Adjust the mirrors, the seat, and the radio, and put on your glasses and seat belt—*then* switch on the ignition.

**Be patient with a diesel.**
Don't try to start the engine when it's cold until you get the green light. If the engine is cold as you try to start, you'll lose fuel that goes through the engine unburned. The engine will run at less than full power and require excess fuel to go as fast as you'd like it to.

*"Full tank?"*

**Don't drive when you're angry or upset.**
You can almost tell from a distance when a driver is upset: He guns the engine, spins the wheels when starting up, slams on the brakes, takes corners on two wheels, and exhibits other wasteful mannerisms. Calm down before driving.

**Drive only in warm weather.**
Of course this is not always possible, but the difference in mileage between driving in 70-degree weather and in 20-degree weather is 1.5 mpg. During winter in the north country, it pays to drive during the warmer daylight hours rather than after the sun goes down and temperatures drop.

**Warm up a cold engine quickly.**
After 30 seconds of idling, even in the coldest weather, your car should be ready to roll. Don't waste time and gasoline by letting the car idle longer than that. Of course, a cold car should be driven slowly at first so the engine can lubricate itself completely before being run at high speeds. Don't start your car on a cold morning and let it idle for minutes while you wait for the heater to warm up the interior. This is wasteful and may be harmful to engine parts that might not be getting proper lubrication. On warm days, or whenever the engine is warmed up, start rolling right away.

**Learn how to use your manual choke.**
Most American-made cars have automatic chokes; however, some imports have manual ones. The manual choke knob should be pulled out when the car is started and left out for a time until the engine warms up. Then it should be pushed in. Leaving it out makes your air-fuel mixture too rich and wastes fuel.

**Avoid vapor lock.**
When the engine is hot and the temperature outside is very hot, you can avoid vapor lock effects by flooring the accelerator pedal as you start the engine. Don't pump the accelerator, just press it to the floor as the starter is engaged. This technique will get the engine going quickly, and avoid prolonged cranking and its attendant gas usage. Any time the engine balks in starting in very hot weather after a long drive, this technique is called for.

**Fill your tank only when ¾ empty.**
That saves you weight—six pounds for each gallon you leave out—and gives the other guy a chance to get his, too. If you always top off your tank, you're driving around with too much weight in the car, and hoarding gas that your neighbor might need.

**Don't go out of your way for fuel.**
Make fuel stops on your way to other destinations; don't make a special trip just to gas up. You might use a gallon of fuel just getting to the gas station and back.

**Buy gas in the morning or on a cool day.**
You get more for your money when the temperature is low, because gas, like other liquids, expands when heated and contracts when cool. At low temperatures versus high temperatures, more gas will go into your tank, even though the pump meter will read the same in both cases.

**Use the best gasoline for your car.**
You don't need premium unless your engine knocks, so a lower-grade no-lead might do just as well. If you own an import that can run on regular leaded gas, use that type. On some cars, the ignition timing is set too far ahead and that causes pre-ignition knock, which premium gasoline is designed to eliminate. You might be able to back off the timing slightly to eliminate the knock while losing little in fuel economy and be able to use regular grades of unleaded gas.

**Use the lowest octane you can.**
If your engine knocks excessively, you might have to use a high-octane fuel. If your engine knocks only during rapid acceleration but runs knock-free most of the time, you can get along on the grade that's in your tank. A little bit of knock—the kind that occurs only when the engine is laboring up hills, when passing, when accelerating with a loaded car or when pulling a trailer—won't hurt. Knock is the rattling noise like a handful of steel balls being dropped on a steel plate that you hear in the engine when you accelerate. A little is a sign that your car is running at its peak timing for efficiency; too much knock can damage your engine's internal parts.

*"Regular...lead-free...gasohol...alcohol...anything!"*

**Buy self-serve gas.**
In some areas of the country, the price of gasoline at a self-service pump is a few cents lower than that at a full-service pump. If you don't need your windshield cleaned, get out of your car and pump your own gas. (By doing so, you'll be able to control the exact amount of gasoline that goes into your tank. This is important if you're going to be figuring your miles per gallon.)

**Make sure the pump reads zero.**
Before filling up your tank at a self-serve pump or letting the service station attendant fill it for you, be sure that the meter on the pump reads zero.

**Keep a record of gas prices in your area.**
Each time you pass a service station that appears to be selling gasoline for a relatively low price, write down the location. Then the next time you need gas, you'll know where to buy it without shopping around.

**Use gasohol.**
If you make some adjustment to the engine, you can use a blend of alcohol and gasoline. Be certain your engine is set up to take the additive: You may have to change the timing, reset the carburetor, and change the compression ratio—a job that could run

*"Why don't you just let the government develop gasohol?"*

you as much as $200 to $300. Gasohol may eat through your fuel line hoses and rubber gaskets too, so you'll have to watch for leaks.

**Don't use your air conditioner.**
Or use it just on special occasions, such as when you're dressed up to go someplace fancy. An air conditioner in operation while a car is moving slowly, such as in city traffic, can reduce mileage by as much as 2.5 mpg; at highway speeds, the decrease might be as little as 0.5 mpg, but even this can be significant over the course of a long trip.

**Dial up the air conditioner.**
You can dial up the air conditioning thermostat in your car. Set the automatic temperature control to a 78-degree rating and you'll save all the energy that would be needed to run the system down to 65 or 70 degrees. In manually operated air conditioning systems, set the temperature slightly higher than usual to cut down on compressor time.

**Close the windows.**
Open windows catch the air stream and slow down a car. Professional car testers close the windows when measuring the performance of a car, especially in acceleration, because of the effect an open window has on wind drag. The smaller the car, the greater this effect; many tiny-engine economy cars noticeably lose performance when the windows are open. That means fuel is being wasted.

**Use the air vents.**
Most new cars have a first-class air ventilation system that can keep air inside the car fresh and cool in hot weather without air conditioning. Learn how it operates best and use this system in hot weather. Although all cars have an exhaust device to permit air to flow through the interior easily, you might try opening rear vent windows slightly or rolling down the rear windows a crack to promote the air flow. Be certain to read your owner's manual for the best operation of the air ventilation system. In some systems—notably Chrysler's newest—you have to turn on the air conditioning system first, then pull out the AC push button to activate the ventilation system and at the same time shut off the air conditioner.

**Turn off the heater water in the summer.**
This is a bit of a chore for so little gain, but every little bit helps. Turn off the pump that circulates water through the heater. That means less of a load on the engine.

**Leave the lights off when they're not needed.**
The load put on a car's generator to power the headlights increases fuel consumption. You can sometimes hear the engines of small cars begin to lug as the headlights are turned on. Be sure to use the lights for optimal visibility, but don't turn them on before you have to.

**Take off your shoes.**
Especially the one on your right foot, since it does all the work with the accelerator. A bare foot will be more precise in using gas than a shod one. Think of it this way: When you wear heavy winter boots, your feel of the accelerator is almost nil; you simply press hard on the pedal when accelerating and let off to slow down. The movements are extreme and very wasteful. A shoeless foot can more easily feel the movement of the accelerator. Extra miles per gallon

are the result: The improvement in city traffic mileage could be more than 1 mpg.

**Think of a fresh egg.**
If you visualize a raw egg between your right foot and the accelerator pedal, you'll be using a good rule of fuel economy. Apply pressure on the accelerator pedal so smoothly that you wouldn't break the shell of that egg.

**Don't jiggle your foot.**
On long trips where steady speeds can be maintained, lock your right foot against the transmission tunnel as you press the accelerator pedal. This prevents the up-and-down motion that can be transmitted to your foot by the motion of the car over the roadway. With a steady foot on the accelerator, just the right amount of gas is fed through the carburetor without any pumping of the carburetor's accelerator pump. On most cars, the slight jiggling of the driver's foot on the accelerator is enough to activate the accelerator pump and waste gas. When you stop this fluctuation, you stop extra squirts of gas from going into the engine. Keep a steady foot on the pedal, and mileage will improve.

**Don't spin your wheels.**
Any time you use your engine at higher speeds and higher loads than called for in traffic, you're wasting gasoline. Spinning your wheels by accelerating too fast might make your car look powerful, but *you* are going to look careless.

**Don't rock around the clock.**
That is, don't spend too many minutes rocking your car when you get stuck in snow or mud. If you can't rock yourself out right away, turn off the engine. Prepare for such a predicament by carrying a small shovel and some salt in your trunk. Use them and a bit of elbow grease instead of gasoline to get going again.

**Use someone else's electricity.**
When camping out in a van or travel trailer, pay the fee charged by the camp owner and plug into the camp's electrical system instead of using your on-board generator to power your electrical appliances.

*"I said, 'I'm closed,'...Now let go of the pump!"*

**Speed up, slow down gradually.**
Flooring the accelerator or using the brakes hard means that you are wasting gas. Try to be the smoothest driver around. Flow with the traffic when necessary; but when it's possible, set your own gradual, steady pace—even if other (more wasteful) drivers pass you by.

**Take turns slowly.**
All other things being equal, your mileage would be higher than it is now if you could always travel in a straight line. When you must turn, turn at low speeds. Any time you hear your tires squeal in a turn, you know you're going too fast and are losing energy.

**Keep off the brake.**
Many drivers either ride the brake pedal or punch it often, as evidenced by the brake lights you see flashing in high-speed traffic. Every time you hit the brake pedal you throw away energy from the engine. The harder you press on the brake pedal when stopping, the more your mileage suffers. Fuel-conscious drivers stop smoothly.

**Before returning a rental car, fill it up yourself.**
Many car rental companies have their own gas pumps, but gas from these pumps is often priced

very high. Fill up the car at a station where gas is relatively inexpensive before you take it back to the rental agency. And keep in mind that you don't have to fill the tank right up to the neck—just make sure the fuel gauge reads full.

**When renting a car, rent a small one.**
Ask for an efficient model, because you'll have to buy gas for it. Make sure to deal with a rental company that can guarantee you a small car. (Some of them quickly rent out all their small cars and then offer you a larger car for the same rental fee. That might seem like a good deal until you have to fill it up.)

**Stay off the manual clutch.**
The engine runs excessively fast to make the car move at any speed if the clutch is slipping. When you press the clutch pedal, or even simply rest your foot on it, you loosen the connection between the engine and the driving wheels. Mileage drops. Also, the clutch wears out quickly.

**Slow down on dirt, gravel, and other rough roads.**
You lose traction on such surfaces. Slow down to give your tires a better chance to grip firmly.

**Don't go too slow.**
It's best to travel at 30 to 35 mph if you want optimal fuel economy. At lower speeds a car engine lugs along and does not deliver its best mileage. Moving at 20 mph in high gear is definitely a losing proposition, so keep your speed up higher when possible. Over 35 mph, you start to lose again; that's what makes 30-35 a happy medium.

**Watch your tach.**
By referring to your car's tachometer, you can keep your engine speed relatively low. Try to maintain engine speeds below 3000 rpm—preferably in the 1400-2000 range—for best economy.

**Maintain a steady speed.**
Once you reach your desired speed, keep it steady. If you let your speed vary up and down by 5 mph, you'll reduce economy by as much as 1.3 mpg. (Of course, this does not count when driving in hilly country where you must adjust your speed to climb and descend hills.

**Watch your vacuum gauge.**
If you're serious about saving gas, a dashboard-mounted vacuum gauge is almost a requirement. Pay attention to what it tells you: when the engine is working hard and using big amounts of fuel, and when it's loafing along and saving fuel. The beauty of a vacuum gauge is that it tells you instantly how you're doing, and it works at all speeds.

**Get into high quickly.**
The sooner you shift into high gear, whether you use a manual or an automatic transmission, the sooner you'll be able to travel most economically. Shift into high or let your automatic shift into third gear at 30-35 mph. Once into high, ease the speed upward; don't floor the accelerator to accelerate quickly. That just wipes out all the gains you make in high gear.

**Trick your automatic.**
As you accelerate to over 30 mph, ease off the accelerator pedal a bit to allow the automatic transmission to shift into high gear earlier than it would otherwise. Once it has shifted, continue accelerating if you must to reach your desired speed. Without such an easing off, the transmission will remain in a lower, less economical, gear until you reach a higher speed.

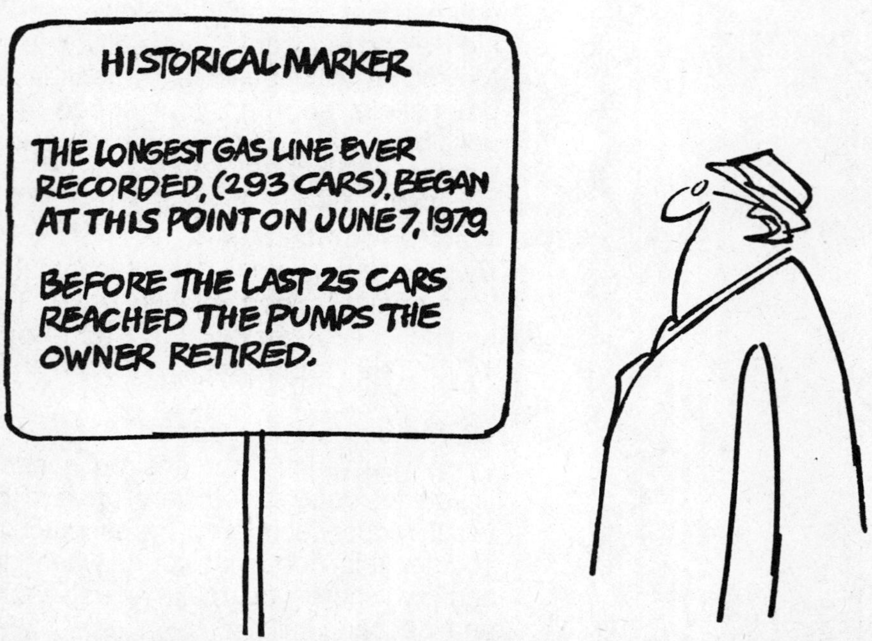

**Skip a gear.**
Now and then you'll be able to shift your manual transmission from second to fourth or from first to third without going through the intermediate gear. Do it. Some traffic conditions will force you to overspeed in a lower gear. When that happens, don't repeat the waste by shifting to the next-highest gear. Instead, match the speed of the car to the gear setting, skip a gear when possible, and go directly to a higher one. When merging into freeway traffic, drivers sometimes speed up in a low gear. Once at the speed limit, they can shift directly to the highest gear and cruise easily in the flow of traffic.

**Use overdrive.**
Overdrive, a higher-than-high gear available on many cars having manual transmission, and some Ford and Lincoln-Mercury cars equipped with automatic, saves gas every time it is used. You can use it even at city speeds. Overdrive becomes especially economical on the highway.

**Merge smoothly.**
Learn to merge onto freeways by accelerating smoothly. Don't come to a stop at the end of the entrance ramp and then stomp on the accelerator pedal.

**Don't be a tailgater.**
Don't accept too readily the notion that "drafting" the vehicle ahead of you can increase your mileage. The notion is often true, but often too dangerous to risk. You simply can't predict what the vehicle ahead of you will do.

**Use a speed-control device when the road is flat.** Speed control can be a real gas saver when you drive long, relatively flat stretches of freeway. The speed control can do a good job of keeping a steady pressure on the accelerator pedal. That means extra miles per gallon. Use of a speed control can be relaxing and enable you to concentrate on other fuel-saving techniques.

**Avoid using speed control in some situations.** Don't use it in hilly terrain, on wet or snow-covered roads, when pulling a trailer or when driving in the city. Speed controls are fine sometimes, but they can't match the average driver when it comes to saving gas in many driving conditions. Going up hills, automatic speed controls often floor the accelerator, and that's bad for economy. Going down hills, they slow down the engine so that the car realizes no gain from the force of gravity. When snow or rain covers the roadway, the speed control pays no attention to wheel slip, but automatically speeds up the engine as the wheels lose traction and the car slows down. This not only wastes fuel, but can be dangerous too. When pulling a trailer, all the problems listed above are magnified, since the speed control must overcome the inertia of an additional 1,000 to 6,000 pounds and work the engine that much harder. And in city traffic there's no way to maintain a constant speed for more than a few blocks, but a speed control will try—and increase fuel consumption.

**Slow down when it's windy.**
Wind from any direction can greatly affect your mileage. If the wind is coming from behind you as you drive, you're in luck: This will boost your mileage. But if you must head into the wind, your economy will suffer. Crosswinds also cause problems because they increase the side-to-side rubbing of the tires against the pavement. You can't always plan your driving for days when the air is still, but you can slow down when you must fight the wind.

**Pick a lane and stay in it.**
Don't do a lot of lane changing—it's far more economical to keep your car going in a straight line than it is to take a zig-zag course.

**Don't weave in and out of traffic.**
That causes side forces on your tires and robs your car of the power the engine is delivering. Also, such weaving often requires unnecessary speeding up and slowing down—two good ways to waste fuel.

**Don't follow a school bus.**
Buses make frequent stops that force you to stop. Each time you do, you waste gas. If you find that your regular route often puts you behind such a slow-moving vehicle, change your route or your departure time.

**Coast down hills.**
Take full advantage of gravity. As you start down a hill, ease up on the accelerator and let your car coast. Try to keep your speed within the posted limit without using your brakes. Keep in mind that the faster you coast, the lower your gain in mileage.

**Don't shut off the engine while moving.**
When coasting down a hill or toward a stoplight, be sure to keep the engine running. It is needed for control of the car. Remember that power brakes and power steering depend on the engine for help.
Also, in most modern cars, you can inadvertently lock up your steering wheel as you turn off the ignition. That could get you into serious trouble. The little fuel you'll save by turning off the engine while the car is moving is not worth the risk of an accident.

**Plan ahead for traffic lights.**
Most traffic lights are set up to change in rhythm with the flow of traffic. Take advantage of this by reaching a steady speed that will allow you to hit all the green lights.

**Check the traffic ahead.**
As you approach a stop sign, consider the number of cars lined up ahead of you. Coast slowly to a stop if that prevents waiting in line. Make a complete stop once and be on your way.

**Don't stop for red lights.**
We don't advocate breaking the law. Just anticipate the red lights, slow down before you get to the intersection, and accelerate gradually as the light turns green.

**Learn how to stop for a red light.**
As soon as you know that you're going to have to stop for a red light, slow down gradually and coast to a stop if possible. Be considerate of other drivers and keep moving, but try to keep off the brakes as much as possible. Take your foot off the accelerator as soon as you realize that the red has you caught.

**Don't use the engine to brake the car.**
Downshifting a manual transmission is for race drivers, not for fuel-conscious drivers. Use your brakes. When you use the engine for braking, it runs at a faster speed than needed and burns more gas with every unnecessary revolution.

**Don't race your engine at a stoplight.**
When waiting for a traffic light to change, take your foot off the accelerator. Don't rev your engine unnecessarily.

**Have the correct toll change ready.**
Keep a supply of coins ready for the tollbooths if you're a regular tollroad user. You'll be able to slip through the booths quickly, without having to wait for change.

**Don't stop to pick up a toll ticket.**
Many times you can glide through a tollbooth area without stopping by simply opening your window ahead of time and putting your hand out to receive

the toll ticket from the attendant. Slow down to 2 or 3 mph—about walking speed—get your ticket, and continue on your way. Most toll attendants will put the ticket into your hand without a hitch, and without forcing you to stop.

**Use neutral when stopped.**
Even when stopped just momentarily for a traffic light, slip the transmission lever into neutral. This takes the load of the transmission off the engine and cuts gas consumption. This is especially important when the air conditioner is being used: Your engine will idle easier in neutral, and handle the drag of the air conditioner with less strain.

**Don't idle at idle.**
When you stop for 30 seconds or more, turn off the engine. That doesn't mean you must shut down at every red light. Most lights stay red for less than 30 seconds. Restarting the engine after a shutdown of such short duration uses more gas than is saved during the down time. At train crossings turn the engine off as soon as you stop, then look to see how long the wait will be. When you must wait in line for access to a parking lot or outdoor bank teller, or—heaven forbid—to buy a tankful of gas, turn off the ignition.

**Use your brakes on upgrades.**
Don't use the clutch or automatic transmission to hold your car in place. Use of anything but the brake means you're burning fuel unnecessarily.

**Come to a complete stop before backing up.**
Don't use the engine to reverse the direction of the car; instead, use the brakes to come to a complete stop.

**Park quickly.**
In a parking lot or along a city street, don't cruise around for several minutes looking for the space that will put you closest to your destination. Find a spot—any spot—quickly and park in it, even if this means you have to walk a few extra steps.

**Don't idle when you get out of the car.**
When you stop to make a phone call or dash into a store for something, turn off the engine. Don't let your car sit at idle, staying warm in the winter or cool on a hot summer day. Before you get out of the car for practically any reason, turn the engine off.

**Turn off heavy-draw accessories before shutting off the engine.**
This means the air conditioning system, for example, will be shut off when you go to start the car up again, and you will gain a few seconds of relief from its drag on the engine.

**Put the car away right away.**
Coming home in the evening, put your car in a spot from which it needn't be moved again until the next day. Restarting a car to spot it for the night is very wasteful, since the car will have cooled down and will run on a gas-rich mixture for the short time it is moving. (This habit is also murder on engine parts.)

**Park in a garage.**
The moderating effect of parking in a garage works in your favor both summer and winter. In summer, the shade cools the car's interior so you don't have to turn on the air conditioner immediately. In winter, your engine stays warmer in a garage than it does outside, so it starts more quickly and requires less time to warm up.

**Don't prime the carburetor.**
Don't rev the engine up to speed before turning it off for the night. You probably don't need to prime the carburetor this way, and the gas you pump into it will evaporate overnight, anyway.

**Check your mileage often.**
This is a good indicator of your progress in cutting consumption, and can be a tipoff to a need for maintenance. If your mileage suddenly goes down by 1 or 2 mpg, something may be wrong with your car.

**Keep a record.**
It's a must if you want to check on your progress. You'll have fun recording how you're improving your economy. Dieters find that such a record helps them to lose weight. You're on a low-gasoline diet, right?

**Make economy a contest.**
Make a game of saving gas; don't think of it as drudgery. See how many miles you can squeeze out of a gallon of gas. Check your progress against the highly optimistic Environmental Protection Agency highway mileage for your car and see if you can better it.

*"I'm even, so make sure he has an odd plate"*

**Shop and pay your bills by mail.**
Instead of driving to a far-away shopping center to buy something, obtain a catalog from the store and order through the mail. Instead of driving to the utility company to pay your bill, spend 15 cents on a stamp and mail your check. These days, 15 cents doesn't buy much gasoline.

**Buy a moped or a small motorcycle.**
These vehicles, which can offer mileage many times greater than that available from even the most efficient automobile, can be used for errand running.

**Vacation at home.**
Surely there are plenty of nearby attractions that you haven't visited. Explore them and save the gasoline you'd need to travel far away.

**Join or form a car pool.**
The advantages are so obvious that they hardly need repeating. By joining a three-person pool, you can triple your mileage. One of the best ideas to come from pooling is the part-drive, part-pool system: You drive to a central point near a freeway, for example, park your car and meet your fellow pool members each morning. At night after work, you return to the parking lot and drive your car the few miles home. This is great for suburban residents. Car pools are also helpful in the city, even for people who live near their work place.

**Urge your employer to encourage car pools.**
You'll see a big decrease in your fuel bills, and your boss probably will see an increase in your productivity because you won't be so worried about finding and paying for gas.

**Move closer to work.**
This is an obvious solution that we lost sight of during the years of low-cost fuels.

**Buy a bicycle.**
You can run many errands on a bike and avoid taking the car out of the garage.

**Check bus and train schedules.**
At least one day a week, you might be able to take public transportation. That will significantly lower your fuel costs.

**Don't drive.**
You don't use any gas if you don't use a car at all. On trips to the corner store, to church or school, either walk or take up bike riding. There is no better way to improve your mileage, and your physical fitness will improve too. If you automatically head for the car when you leave the house, you need to do some fresh thinking on the subject of short trips.

# PART TWO:

# MAINTAINING YOUR CAR

Keeping your car in good mechanical condition is one of the easiest ways to get the best mileage your car can deliver. And car maintenance itself is easier than ever today. Compared with the recommended maintenance schedules of just 10 years ago, today's cars can go thousands of extra miles between routine service checks. Some service items that used to need attention every few thousand miles—chassis lubes, distributor points, brake adjustments, and wheel bearing repacking—have been eliminated altogether by technical advances such as sealed-for-life chassis points, breakerless electronic ignition systems, self-adjusting brakes, and sealed wheel bearings.

Unfortunately, today's cars are also more complicated than the cars of the 1950s and '60s. This means the days of the "shade tree" mechanic are almost over. Most car owners just don't have the specialized knowledge or equipment necessary to service their autos properly. For example, on newer cars the timing and carburetor adjustments are very precise and must be made exactly according to manufacturers' specifications in order to comply with stringent exhaust emission limits. Usually, such adjustments are best left to a trained mechanic. Some components, like spark plugs, are no longer easily accessible because of the additional equipment found on today's cars that wasn't even available on the cars of yesteryear. Items like power steering pumps, air conditioning compressors and belt systems, large-capacity radiators, and electric cooling fans crowd the space under the hoods of most modern cars and complicate servicing.

Today's extended mileage intervals can result in a small problem going undetected by the owner for a long time. What started out as a minor fault can turn into a costly service headache. For this reason, many people like to have their cars checked more frequently than specified in the owner's manual.

Today's cars are designed to run safely and reliably provided the recommended routine maintenance is performed when it should be. It pays to read and follow the recommended service instructions in your owner's manual. Check your car's engine compartment periodically for signs of anything unusual, like a loose wire or hose. And be sure to check fluid levels regularly. If you notice a sudden drop in gas mileage or an unusual noise, make a note of it, and have it checked right away. You'll not only have peace of mind; you may save money in the long run.

"Think upkeep," and you'll keep up your mileage.

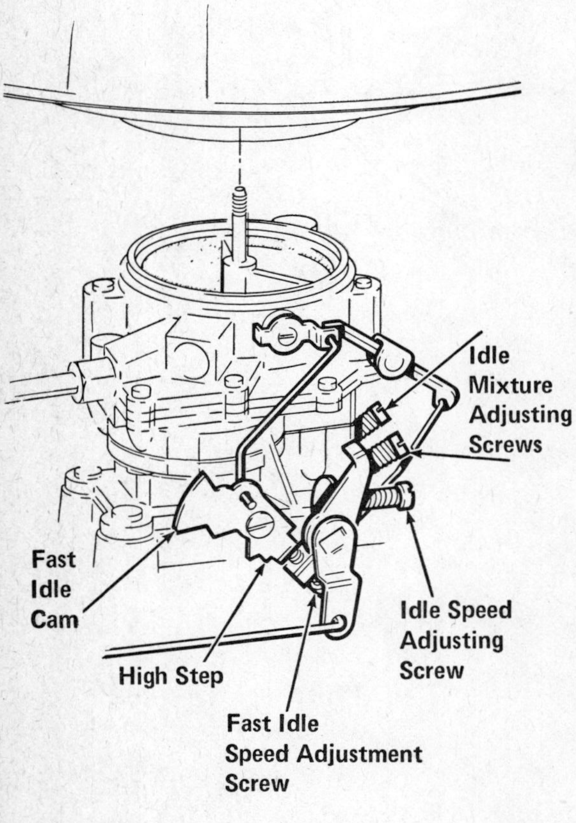


*Main adjustment points in a typical modern carburetor.*

**Get a tune-up.**
This is perhaps the most important maintenance tip, but one frequently delayed or overlooked. Recommended intervals between tune-ups vary widely nowadays due to the advent of electronic ignition and unleaded gas, but all cars need regular engine maintenance. Read your owner's manual for recommended tune-up schedules. A tune-up can mean a 9 to 15 percent improvement in fuel economy. (One of our sources says the savings can be as high as 20 percent.)

**Check carburetor adjustment.**
On newer cars there is little, if any, latitude for adjusting the carburetor, but on older cars this can be a frequent necessity. You may need a professional to make this adjustment, and he may tell you that you need a tune-up as well in order for the carburetor adjustments to "hold." It's true that carburetor efficiency depends on other systems working well, so a tune-up may indeed be in order. Problems with maladjusted carburetors include uneven idling, fast idling, stalling when cold, and low power on acceleration—all of which hamper fuel economy.

**Have your compression checked.**
If your car runs unevenly or seems to have lost power, it may be that your engine has lost compression. That means the energy from your fuel is not being fully used. Check your car's compression and make sure you're using gas as efficiently as possible.

**Clean the carburetor.**
You can buy commercial carb cleaners that will help improve the way the engine runs, but they're seldom needed and will not fix a car that has problems with burned valves and worn camshafts. Try a cleaner once; if it works, fine. But don't become addicted to these additives.

*"...She's very capable...fixed her own carburetor on the way to work..."*

**Wash your engine.**
Dirt and oil accumulated on the engine will cause it to retain heat. An engine that runs hot runs inefficiently.

**Don't tinker with carburetor settings.**
Just make certain the carburetor is set to the manufacturer's specifications. Change the setting too drastically and you'll dramatically lower your mileage.

**Keep the injectors clean.**
These super-accurate carburetors of fuel injection systems can be easily clogged by dirt particles. If your fuel-injected engine runs rough or misfires, the injectors may be at fault. Check your fuel filter first; if it is dirty or defective, your injectors should be inspected.

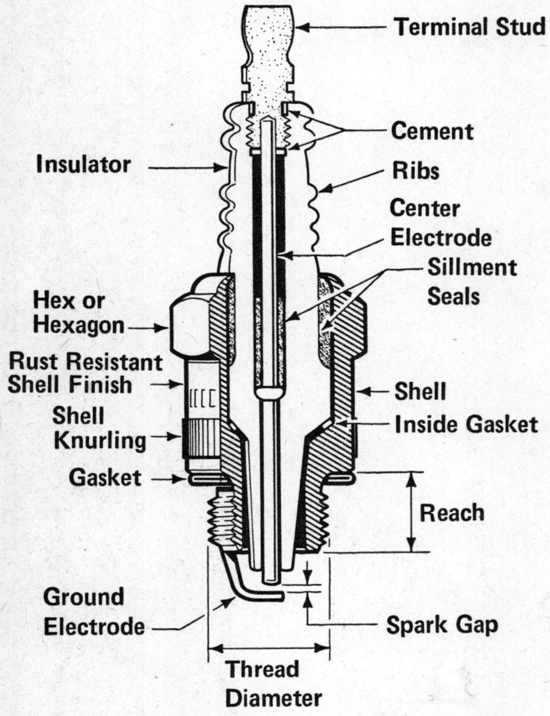


*Anatomy of a spark plug.*

**Change spark plugs promptly.**
Don't wait until the engine misfires; take the old plugs out on schedule. If one plug out of eight is misfiring, you're losing one-eighth of the engine's output. Even if the engine misfires on one cylinder for only a short period at start-up when cold, you're running raw gasoline out the exhaust pipe each time the crankshaft turns around.

**Check distributor cap.**
If your car starts slowly in wet weather, you may have a little crack in the distributor cap where moisture leaks in and shorts out the ignition system. Take the cap off and look at it against a bright light. If it is damaged, it will decrease your mileage more than a fouled spark plug.

**Replace points.**
If the points start to deteriorate, all your spark plugs will be affected. Fuel economy can drop precipitously as the misfiring engine coughs, stumbles, hesitates, and balks at start-up.

**Check ignition coil output.**
A faulty coil can act up at certain speeds and be affected by the weather. A simple check can correct this fuel-wasteful fault.

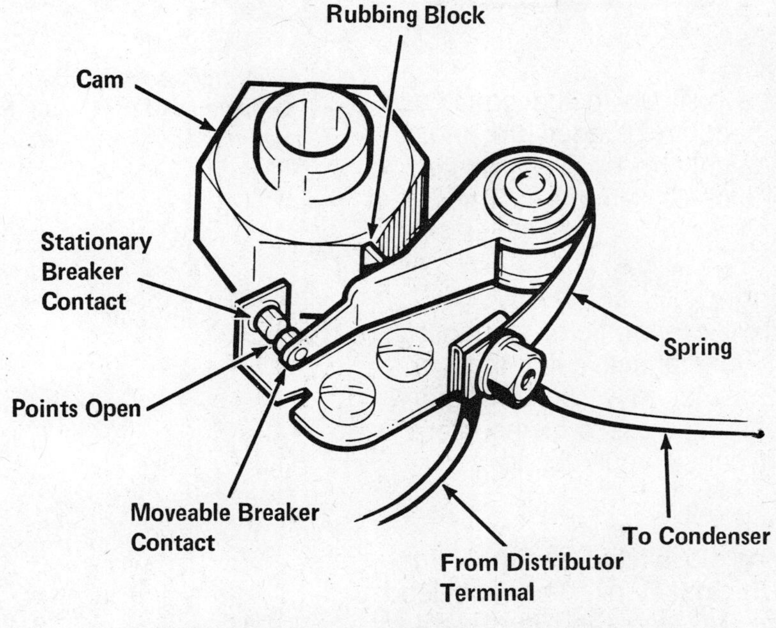


*Detail drawing of a distributor point assembly*

**Replace air filter.**
This depends greatly on where you drive. In the Southwest, where dry weather and a lot of sand make for dusty conditions, an air filter will get dirty fast and may need changing or cleaning as often as once a month; in the East where paved roads might be all your car ever sees, a filter can last for many months or even years without change. A filter that is clogged cuts off air to the engine. This is a detriment to good fuel economy. Tip-offs to a clogged filter are a loss of power and a general feeling that the engine is not getting a chance to perform the way it should.

**Clean fuel filter.**
In gasoline-fueled cars, a clogged fuel filter will cut down on the free flow of gasoline to the carburetor and reduce economy. Clean the filter or replace it and immediately see gas consumption go down.

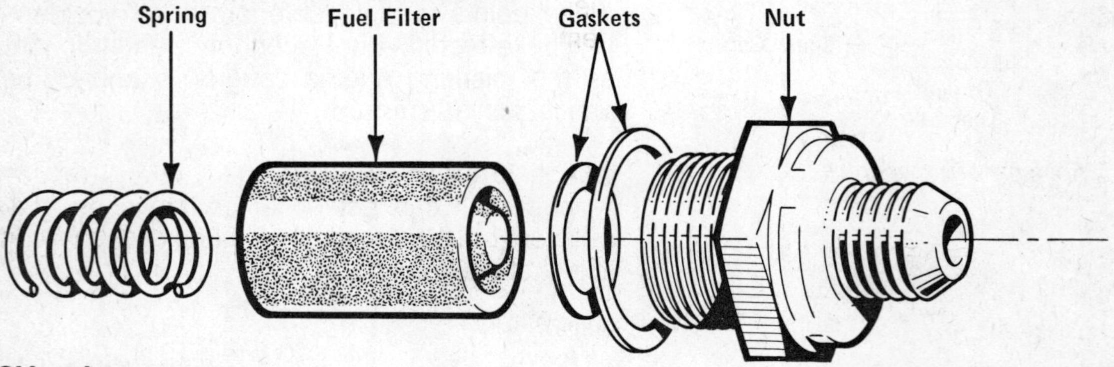


*Fuel filter assembly housed in the carburetor as used on GM cars. Only the filter elements need to be cleaned or replaced.*

**Service PCV valve.**
This little part allows gases built up in the crankcase to be burned. Allow it to become plugged up and high pressure will work against the engine's power. It is easy to service: 10 minutes to remove it, rinse it in gasoline, and replace it.

**Use gas additives sparingly.**
Don't use gasoline treatment preparations to boost your mileage. They aren't very effective for that. However, they can absorb water in your car's fuel system. This water, sometimes present in the storage tanks at gas stations, can cause your car to stall.

**Don't run on empty.**
If you do, you risk dredging up all the sediment that collects at the bottom of the gas tank. This can lead to a clogged fuel filter and gas line, and inefficient operation of the engine.

**Free up charcoal canister hoses.**
If they are blocked, you're losing gasoline. It's just evaporating into the air. Make certain that all your emission control systems are clean and working. They are tied closely to your fuel economy.

**Inspect the automatic choke.**
When the choke is operating, mileage drops by as much as 25 percent. You need the choke in cold weather until the engine warms up. The faster it turns off, the more gas you'll save. Have it checked if your engine idles fast after it is fully warmed up. (Fuel-injection and diesel engines have no chokes.)

**Inspect the heat riser.**
Make sure the heat riser—a thermostatic device located on the engine's manifold—is operating freely. This control, which reduces the amount of time needed for the engine to reach normal operating temperature, has a tendency to rust.

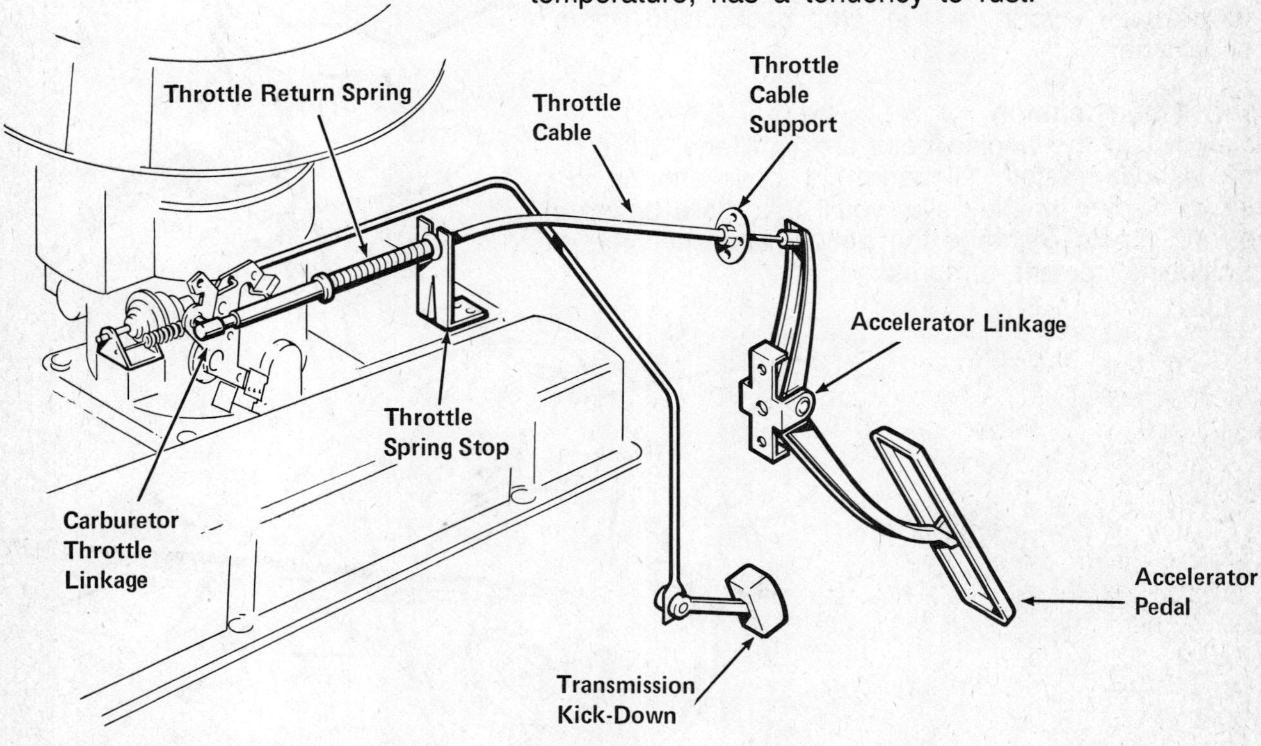


*Diagram of a typical accelerator linkage.*

**Check accelerator linkage.**
Make sure the accelerator reacts quickly to your commands. If your car idles fast or is slow to change speeds when you lift off the accelerator, your linkage may be in need of a lubrication or straightening.

**Check the hoses.**
Believe it or not, hoses should be replaced every two years or 24,000 miles, according to some owner's manuals. Most drivers wait longer, until a leak is discovered. Replacement of faulty hoses is easy and will prevent headaches.

**Keep radiator topped off.**
An engine that runs too hot wastes gas. Keep the coolant up to the top of the radiator. If the cap needs replacement, get a new one. Otherwise, you'll lose coolant and risk overheating.

**Check for oil burning.**
It may be due to worn piston rings or burned-out valve guides in the engine. Blueish exhaust and soot in the tailpipe are tip-offs that you are not getting the fuel economy the car is designed to deliver. Almost invariably, excess burning of oil results in fouled spark plugs, which further cuts economy. Stop the oil loss and watch your mileage jump back up to where it should be.

**Control belt tension.**
Make certain the engine belts are tight enough to work without wasteful slippage, yet loose enough to prevent binding. If they slip, you'll use more power in the long run to recharge the battery and keep the air conditioning coolant compressed.

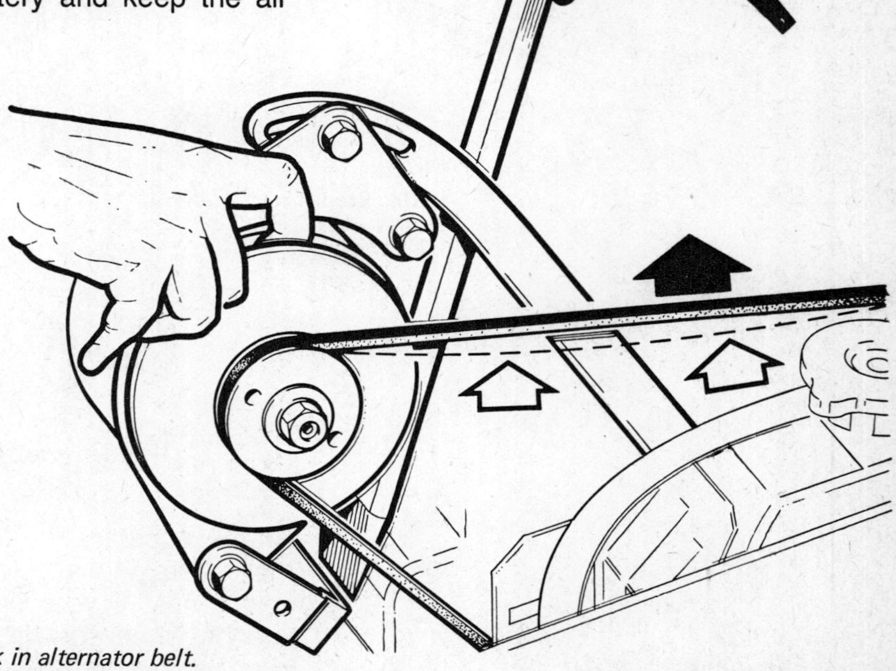

*Adjusting slack in alternator belt.*

*A simple tool for keeping battery terminals clean.*

**Inspect battery.**
Make sure that it's up to the job of getting the engine started quickly and will deliver full power to the spark plugs all the time. Check for corrosion that robs the battery of power, and keep the terminals clean. Make sure there's enough water.

**Keep wiring clean.**
Oil spills under the hood create sticky surfaces that collect dirt and moisture. These act as conductors of electricity, robbing your ignition system of power and frequently causing misfiring of spark plugs. Keep the wires clean—kerosene painted on with a brush and washed off with water is a good way to do so—and you'll get all the electric energy through to the plugs.

**Examine the thermostat.**
A faulty thermostat will delay warm-up of the engine. This wastes gas, since the engine never reaches its most efficient operating temperature. If your heater does not put out hot air within the first five minutes of driving in freezing weather, you should have the thermostat checked.

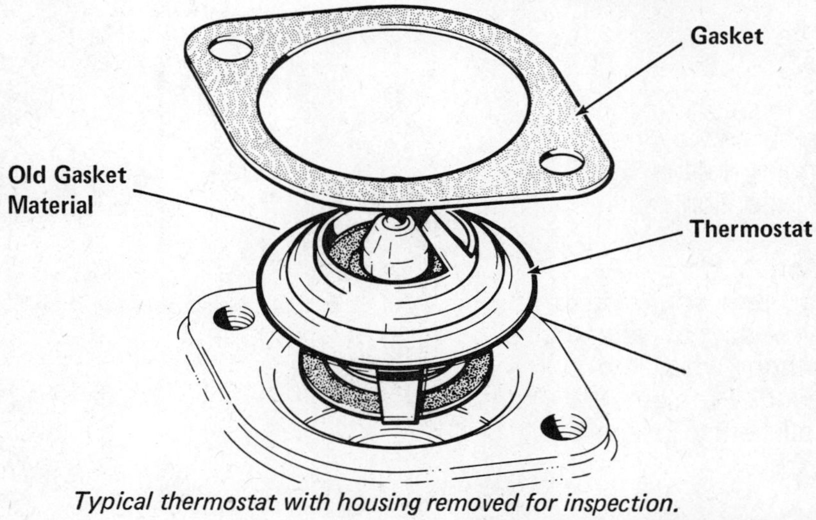


*Typical thermostat with housing removed for inspection.*

**Keep your air conditioner in good shape.**
Air conditioning problems can be costly in terms of repair expense and gasoline consumption. Most such problems are caused by leaks in the system that are due to a drying out of the seals. To avoid this, operate your car's AC for at least 15 minutes every other week, even in winter. Have the system checked out once a year by a qualified air conditioning mechanic to prevent serious problems.

**Examine the automatic transmission.**
Listen to it often when driving to determine if it is slipping, shuddering or otherwise performing poorly. Change the oil in this system according to suggested schedules, being certain to use the recommended lubricant. Regular inspections are very important on newer cars, which use the same transmission fluid for 50,000 or 100,000 miles.

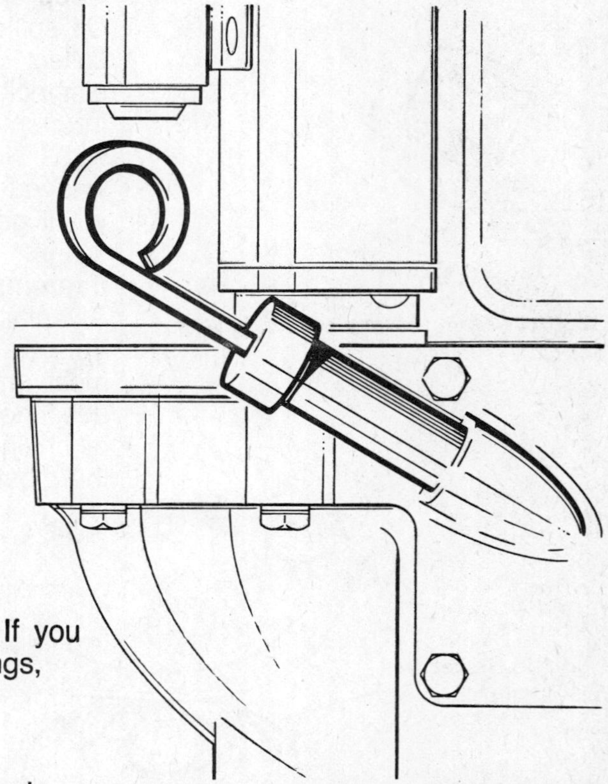

*Dipstick for checking automatic transmission fluid level.*

**Check spin of the wheels.**
They should spin freely when turned by hand. If you hear brake drag or feel a binding in the bearings, your car needs a mechanic's attention.

**Pay attention to a shuddering clutch.**
It means the clutch is slipping, and your engine is running faster than necessary. Also pay attention to differences in the noises you hear when the clutch pedal is depressed and released. Problems with the throwout bearing can cause efficiency losses too.

**Inspect drum brakes.**
Drum brakes should be checked for dirt and corrosion that may cause the brake shoes to drag against the drum. If they drag, the car's engine will always be fighting the brakes, wasting gas.

**Check parking brake cables.**
Rust, dirt, and normal wear can cause a car's parking brake cables to stick. This means the parking brake remains on. That'll reduce your mileage—and the life of your brakes.

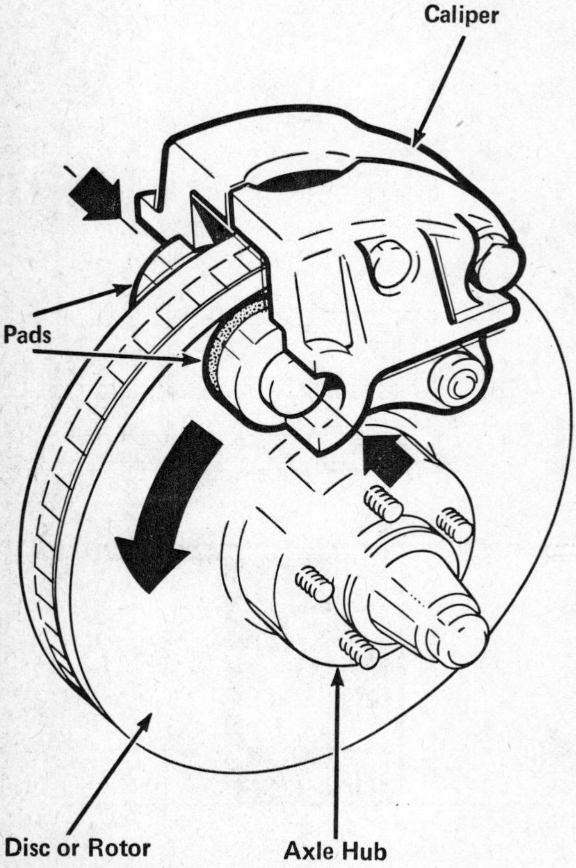

*Disc brake with clearance between brake pad and disc.*

**Don't drive with the parking brake on.**
If you use your parking brake when you park your car, make sure to release it before you start driving again. And don't trust a dashboard "parking brake on" light—the bulb could be burned out. Check the brake handle.

**Fix squeaky brakes.**
Disc brakes have a tendency to drag when the brakes are not being applied. That's wasteful. Make certain your brake calipers are clean and that there is some clearance between the pads and the discs.

**Change axle lubricant.**
The forgotten part of the drive train is the rear axle carrier. When the lubricant runs low it can be merely topped off, but we recommend replacing the lubricant then, since the old lubricant probably will have lost its effectiveness.

**Check the exhaust system for blockage.**
A real fuel economy drain is a constricted exhaust system. Be certain that you are getting all the exhaust space your engine needs. Symptoms of blockage are a decrease in power and/or a whooshing noise in the exhaust. A blocked exhaust system will decrease your mileage more than a fouled spark plug.

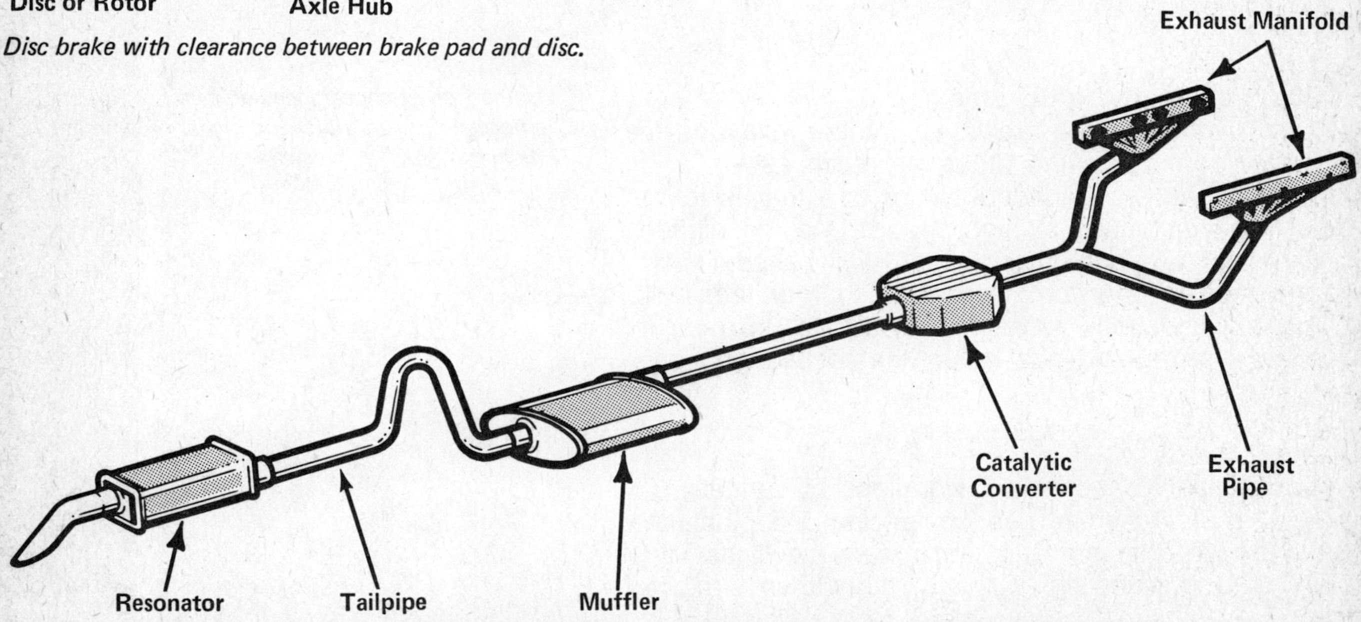

*Diagram of modern exhaust system and key points to check for blockage.*

**Keep wheels in alignment.**
Your front wheels should point slightly inward from the straight-ahead position. Too much toe-in will decrease fuel economy because the tires will scrub against the pavement. On newer cars, the toe-in angle is almost nonexistent, since the auto companies are trying to make the wheels turn as freely as possible. If your car seems to steer peculiarly, it might need an alignment. Get one, and you'll save gas every time you drive.

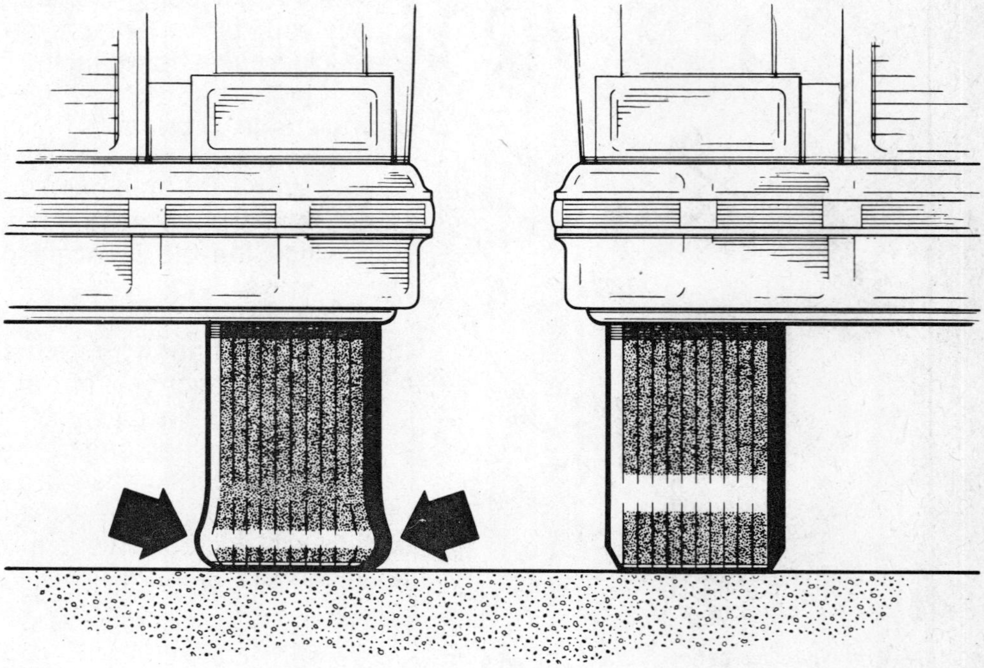

*Comparison of appearance between tires inflated to normal pressure (left) and higher recommended pressure (right).*

**Inflate tires to the high side.**
Usually, two pressures are given for tire inflation: one for an unloaded car; the other, as much as six pounds higher, for a loaded car or one that is to be driven long distances at high speed. Use the higher pressure for all your driving. There will be some deterioration in ride comfort, but the harder tires will roll easier, and you'll save gas. You lose 0.5 mpg if tires are just four pounds below the recommended pressure.

**Balance the tires.**
If your car exhibits constant vibrations at various speeds, your tires may need balancing. Poor balance can set up a shimmy, and that means you'll be traveling in a slight zig-zag path rather than straight ahead.

**Get new tires as needed.**
Bald tires can cause a loss of traction in rainy weather or on slippery surfaces. A good tread grips the roadway well when the going is slick. Use the old Lincoln penny trick to measure the depth of the tread. Stick the penny into the groove of the tread head first. If the top of Lincoln's head is visible, you have too little tread. Loss of traction means wheel spinning and therefore a decrease in fuel economy.

**Remove the snow tires.**
When the weather turns warm, change to the standard tires as quickly as you can. The heavy construction, tread pattern, and weight of snow tires can affect fuel economy adversely. Snow tires also wear faster than standard tires in warm weather, since the rubber compound used for them is not particularly suited to high temperatures.

**Buy oversize tires.**
By using tires that have a large diameter instead of tires that are smaller, you effectively raise the car's gearing. This, like a higher numerical axle ratio, will increase mileage.

**Tighten the gas cap.**
How many times have you seen raw gasoline sloshing out of the car ahead of you as it accelerates? It happens often enough to warrant a check of your own car. Make sure your gas cap is tightened each time you get gas. If you smell raw fuel, inspect the cap and the rest of the car if necessary to see where the odor is coming from.

**Fix dents promptly.**
Dents in the grille and front fenders of a car are air traps that reduce the car's ability to slip efficiently through the air. Dents elsewhere in the body have a lesser but still significant detrimental effect on the car's aerodynamics.

**Knock off the ice and snow.**
In the winter, as snow and ice accumulate on the car, remove it quickly. Its weight can approach 100 pounds. That puts an extra load on the engine.

**Keep your car clean.**
This one might sound like we're stretching things a bit, but it's a fact that the smoother the surface of your car, the more easily it passes through the air. A clean exterior is slipperier than a dirty one.

*The basics of the "Saturday morning car wash."*

**Polish your car.**
Polishing not only keeps your car looking nice; it can help your gas economy. A slippery surface lets you run farther on the same amount of gas.

**Drain off the water.**
Some diesel-engine cars have a fuel filter water trap compartment that can be drained easily. Don't ignore this fuel-economy aid. Fuel oil is notoriously contaminated by water. It's easy to clear if you follow your owner's manual instructions.

**Get an engine block heater.**
These devices are often standard equipment in the north country where super-cold winters turn oil and grease into unyielding masses of goo. An in-block heater will keep the crankcase warm overnight and allow the engine's innards to turn freely when the starter is used. Plug it in far enough ahead to warm up the engine oil and coolant, then start up like it's summertime.

**Don't use heavy lubricants.**
When lubricating the car's parts, just as when changing oil, be sure to avoid too-heavy grease and oil. They slow down the machinery and put a drag on the engine. Cold weather calls for lightweight oils and lubricants.

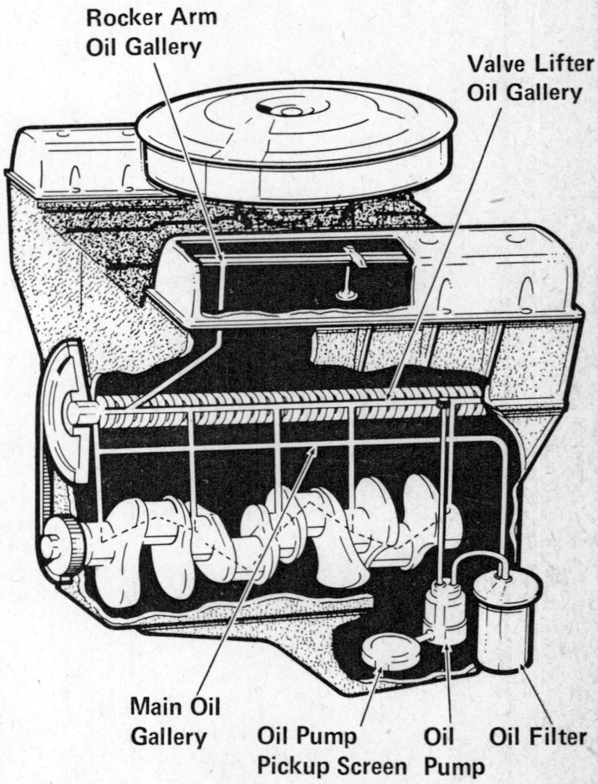

*Major parts of engine's internal lubrication system.*

**Don't purchase an auxiliary fuel tank.**
Because fuel is hard to find sometimes, accessory fuel tanks that can enlarge the car's capacity by 20 or 30 gallons are becoming fashionable. They give the long-distance driver another day or two to find fuel when he's on the road, and let the city driver go an extra week or two between fill-ups. A problem is that the weight of the extra gas lowers your car's mileage. Gasoline weighs six pounds a gallon, so 20 gallons weigh as much as an extra passenger. You could lose as much as 0.4 mile per gallon when using a loaded extra tank. It would be smarter to improve your fuel economy through good driving habits, and leave the extra fuel at the service station. Safety is another important consideration. An extra tank might spring some leaks. The dripping gas could be dangerous. Your car is designed to protect occupants from gasoline fires in an accident, but this design might be ruined when an extra tank is fitted. Modern cars are designed to handle predictably when loaded fully with fuel and passengers as well as when empty except for the driver. By adding weight you can upset the balance of the chassis. When you put an extra 120 pounds or so in the rear, the car becomes tail-heavy, and thus will tend to oversteer and lose traction.

*"Glad to see you have no five dollar limit"*

**Buy a mileage measuring gauge.**
This is good for instant checks of your fuel economy under all driving conditions. Such a gauge can be installed and removed in minutes. It will clearly show the effect on fuel economy of different speeds, weather conditions, and road surfaces.

**Be wary of long-life oils.**
Some of these are said to last for up to 20,000 miles, and are said to work fine in both extremely hot and extremely cold weather. Their claims, if true, could boost fuel economy signficantly, especially in freezing temperatures where they take no time to thin out and therefore allow the engine to run efficiently even when very cold. It appears that these oils are as good as claimed. However, since they have not been certified for the extra mileage, their use may invalidate your engine warranty—which usually calls for oil changes every 6,000 to 7,500 miles.

**Shun platinum-tipped spark plugs.**
These last longer than regular plugs, and cost a lot more. Although some cars have these as standard equipment and recommended change intervals for them go up to 50,000 miles, they, like regular plugs, can become fouled. And fouled plugs can cause fuel economy problems. Use regular plugs instead.

**Avoid "super" spark plugs.**
They cost too much to be really economical in the long run. Stick to plugs recommended by the car maker and change them every two years or so as the owner's manual directs. Buy them at department stores instead of car dealerships and save a lot of money. Learn to install them yourself.

**Vapor injectors sound good, but . . .**
There is some truth to the claim that water vapor injected into an engine will extend mileage. But that occurs in very limited circumstances. For the most part, the engine you get in your new car is best suited to run with the equipment it comes with. Furthermore, use of a vapor injector might invalidate your new-car warranty.

**Don't bother with breather devices.**
They promise a lot but deliver little. These spacers are designed to open up the engine's air-intake system and let the engine take in more air—thus burning gasoline more completely and increasing fuel economy. Their effectiveness has not been proved in long-range tests.

# PART THREE:

# BUYING A NEW CAR

Inflation has eliminated the substantial price advantage import cars once had over domestic products. And with the new generation of "downsized" American cars, vehicle size alone is no longer an accurate guide to gas economy. For example, a subcompact Toyota Corona equipped with the

*"It won't run longer than five minutes"*

standard 134 cubic-inch four-cylinder engine is rated by the Environmental Protection Agency at 18 miles per gallon; the Chevy Malibu, an intermediate, is also rated at 18 miles per gallon equipped with the standard 200 cubic-inch V-6 and automatic transmission. So, before you head for the showroom, decide not just how large a car you need, but also the optional equipment that's most important for the kind of driving you'll do in that car.

Weight is perhaps the biggest enemy of good fuel economy—for a very good reason. A heavier car needs a more powerful (and usually larger-displacement) engine to provide reasonable acceleration and load-carrying ability in a vehicle of a given size. The larger engine in a heavy car can be expected to use more fuel than a smaller engine in a lighter car of the same size.

But don't just order the smallest available engine for the particular model you're considering. An engine without sufficient horsepower for the weight of the car may actually deliver worse mileage than a more powerful engine in that car. After all, the less powerful engine will have to be worked harder to provide performance equal to that of the larger engine. Sometimes there's little difference in mileage ratings among standard and optional engines. For example, the Malibu equipped with the optional 267-cid V-8 and automatic transmission is rated at 18 miles per gallon—exactly the same figure as for the standard engine/transmission in that car.

It's no longer true that you have to sacrifice good mileage for convenience. Several manufacturers now, or will soon, offer new four-speed automatic transmissions in which fourth gear is an overdrive ratio. The overdrive gearing reduces the number of engine revolutions needed to maintain a given road speed compared with a "direct drive" ratio of 1:1. So-called "economy" rear axle ratios, with lower numerical values, can also be expected to deliver better mileage than higher numerical ratios.

Naturally, you'll want your new car to have the balance of size, room, comfort, performance, style, and economy that's right for you. So ask yourself a few questions before you go shopping. For example, do you really use the carrying capacity of a five- or six-passenger car often enough to justify the high running costs of an intermediate or full-size car? Power accessories like air conditioning take their toll in economy by adding weight. How many months out of the year do you really use your car's air conditioning system? Could you learn to live without it? Do you think only a big, heavy car rides smoothly? You may be surprised to find many smaller cars ride just as well as some heavier, less economical cars.

For economy-conscious motorists, there's never been a better selection of new cars to choose from. Perhaps the best suggestion for buying an economical new car is to know what you want, and then to pick the car that offers the best compromise among those features and performance characteristics that are important to you.

**Buy a new car like one of these.**
Here's a list of some of the most fuel-efficient new cars available and their EPA city mileage figures.

Chevrolet Chevette—25
Datsun 310—28
Dodge Challenger (Plymouth Sapporo)—26
Dodge Colt (Plymouth Champ)—33
Dodge Omni (Plymouth Horizon)—25
Fiat Strada—28
Ford Fiesta—28

*1979 Chevrolet Chevette*

*1979 Dodge Omni*

Honda Civic CVCC—28
Renault Le Car—26
Toyota Corolla—24
Volkswagen Rabbit (gas engine)—26

*1979 Honda Civic CVCC*

*1979 Volkswagen Rabbit*

**Buy an economical used car.**
The following used cars have been selected by CONSUMER GUIDE® magazine on the basis of their

*1978 Audi Fox*

*1978 Buick Opel*

*1977 Chevrolet Vega*

*1978 Mazda GLC*

gas mileage only. All cars listed recorded an overall average of at least 25 miles per gallon in our tests or those conducted by the EPA.

1975 Audi Fox—28 mpg
1977 Audi Fox—28 mpg
1978 Buick Opel—25 mpg
1977 Chevrolet Vega—28 mpg
1971-73 Datsun 1200—36 mpg
1974-75 Datsun B-210—25-27 mpg
1978 Datsun B-210—40 mpg
1978 Ford Fiesta—38 mpg
1978 Ford Pinto—29 mpg
1977-78 Honda Accord—32 mpg
1976-77 Honda Civic—30 mpg
1977-78 Mazda GLC—39 mpg
1978 Mercury Bobcat—25 mpg
1978 Plymouth Champ/Dodge Colt—35 mpg
1977 Pontiac Astre—30 mpg
1977 Pontiac Sunbird—30 mpg
1976-78 Renault Le Car—32-36 mpg
1977 Subaru DL and GF—33 mpg
1977-78 Toyota Corolla—28 mpg
1973 Volkswagen Beetle—30 mpg
1978 Volkswagen Dasher—30 mpg
1978 Volkswagen Rabbit Diesel—39 mpg

**Buy a mini-truck instead of a bigger one.**
Before you lay down your money for a big domestic pickup truck, consider one of the more fuel-efficient imports. Many of them can carry a very large payload for their size—perhaps as big a load as you'll ever want to haul.

**Don't buy a too-tall camper.**
If you want a camper for your pickup truck, shop for one that does not stand far above the truck's roof. The lower the camper, the lower the drag.

**Buy a car that can use regular gas.**
There aren't many of these around anymore. All domestic cars and most of the foreign ones now have catalytic converters as part of their emissions-control systems, and therefore can use only no-lead gas. But Honda, Datsun, and other foreign makers still sell cars that can take regular.

**Buy the smallest car you can.**
Don't buy a car that's bigger than you really need. The size of a car makes a huge difference in the mileage you're likely to obtain.

**Curb weight.**
The weight of a car is a big factor in fuel economy. Every additional 500 pounds will cost you another 2 to 2.5 mpg. Other factors like engines, transmissions, and accessories also have a big effect on fuel consumption; but all other things being equal, the lighter the car, the better the mileage. Get a lean car to start with and you're off on the right foot in the fuel economy marathon, no matter how you drive or how the car is equipped.

**Aerodynamic styling.**
Cars are being designed for improved aerodynamic efficiency as well as for beauty. When shopping for a car that will slice through the air easily and therefore help to maximize your mileage, think of the difference between a Volkswagen Beetle and a VW Rabbit. It's easy to see that the newer model was designed to minimize wind resistance. Sloping rooflines, smooth side styling, and sleek lines in general are signs of low drag.

*Modern hatchback styling typical of lighter-weight fuel-efficient cars.*

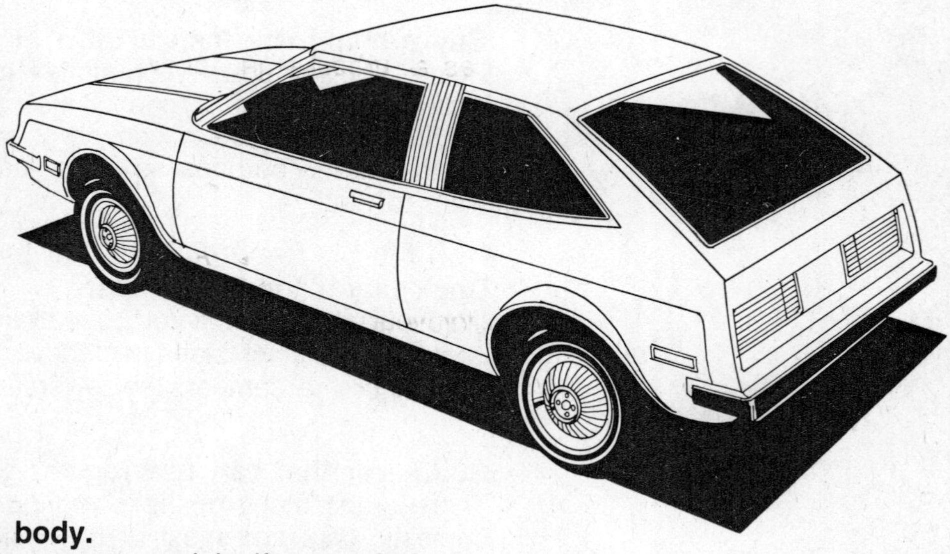

**Select a hatchback body.**
You'll get more load room per weight if you select a hatchback over a conventional notchback body design. Lighter-weight hatchbacks get better fuel economy than comparable or bigger station wagons.

**Engine size.**
You must choose an engine that matches the size and weight of the car. Pick one that's too small and you overwork the engine, never realizing it's fuel economy potential; get one too big and you will burn more gas than you need. Nowadays there are a lot of different engine types to choose from. Although general statements are chancy, here's how we rate them from most economical to least: four-cylinder diesel, four-cylinder gas, four-cylinder turbocharged, five-cylinder diesel, five-cylinder turbocharged diesel, five-cylinder gasoline, six-cylinder diesel, six-cylinder turbocharged diesel, rotary engine (Mazda), six-cylinder gasoline, eight-cylinder gasoline. The engine design is not too important, so you can choose an in-line or V-type six cylinder, or an in-line or opposed four cylinder, with the assurance of similar economy.

**Turbochargers**
Turbochargers work only part of the time, boosting engine power when quick acceleration is needed. Each time the turbo works extra fuel is burned, since the turbo packs a bigger charge of air and fuel into the engine. When the turbo is off—at steady engine speeds—fuel economy is at its maximum. You'll pay a hefty price when you buy a turbo, and every time you use it. Do you really have to accelerate as fast as a turbocharged engine will let you? Probably not.

**Carburetors.**
Some multiple-barrel carburetors get better mileage than single-barrel types, but there's no hard and fast rule. Check the EPA ratings to be sure that the carburetor option on your car is the most economical for your engine size. A four-barrel carburetor might provide better economy than a two-barrel in the same engine.

**Fuel injection.**
If the cost is not out of line with your needs and you want the best fuel economy possible, fuel injection is worthwhile. It's a precise way of metering the fuel that goes into the engine. (The Volkswagen and Audi models with top mileage—including Rabbit, Scirocco, Dasher, and Audi 4000—all have fuel injection.)

## Electronic ignition.

You'll have little choice in another couple of years—that's how completely electronic ignition has been accepted by the auto industry. Advantages include the ability to deliver top fuel economy after many miles of use. No longer do ignition points wear out and cause misfiring at 12,000 miles. Instead, spark plugs get full power all the time, fire more consistently, and burn all the gas the engine receives when used in an electronic ignition system.

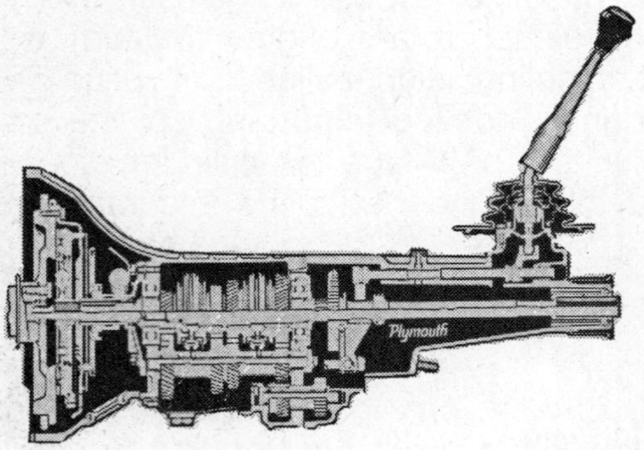


*Cut-away views of economical manual transmissions; four-speed transmission (left) and five-speed transmission (right).*

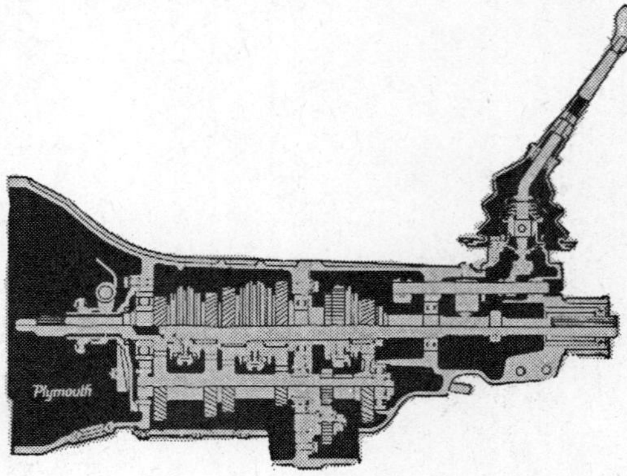


## Manual transmission.

Up to just recently, the growth in popularity of automatic transmissions has been steady. Now many buyers are selecting manual transmissions. The economy advantage of a manual transmission over an automatic is not as great as it once was, but you can still gain 3 to 6 percent in fuel economy by choosing a stick.

## Overdrive.

Overdrive, a fifth gear on manual-transmission cars or fourth gear on Ford's new overdrive automatic transmissions, can boost highway mileage by as much as 20 percent. This is a worthwhile option.

## Limited slip rear axle.

This can improve fuel economy when driving on low-friction surfaces like snow-covered and wet roads. It should be ordered only if you need additional traction for bad-weather driving.

**Axle ratios.**
Generally, if your car's axle ratio is below 3.00:1, you have an economy axle; above that, you have a performance ratio. (Some smaller cars like the Honda Accord, Volkswagen Rabbit, and Renault Le Car have ratios as high as 4.0:1 and still deliver good fuel economy.) The lower the number, the better fuel economy you'll get. This is especially true of big cars like those built in America. For cars with V-8 engines, try to get a 2.7:1 or lower rear axle ratio, because the V8 is big enough to handle the low ratio and still deliver good performance. If you tow a trailer or do heavy-duty city driving, a higher ratio is called for.

**Two-speed axles.**
These are available on only a few cars. They do a good job of stretching your driving range. The Dodge Colt FF and Plymouth Champ imports have slick-shifting two-speed rear axles that provide low-gear performance when you want it, and excellent fuel economy when you choose that. It's an excellent feature of these small Japanese cars, but one that will not see much wider use because the unit is too heavy and too expensive to put on high-production cars right now.

**Four-wheel drive.**
Stay away from this option if you want to save fuel. Four-wheel drive costs you 6 percent or more in fuel usage. Big engines and four-wheel drive combine to give the utility vehicles like Chevy Blazer, Ford Bronco, Plymouth Trail Duster and AMC Jeep the poorest fuel economy of any personal transportation vehicle around.

**Front locking hubs.**
If you want four-wheel drive, be certain to get front wheel locking hubs, and use them to disconnect the front drive machinery when four-wheel drive isn't needed.

**Automatic level control suspension.**
Most of the time, such levelers do not continually adjust the height of your car, and so do not affect fuel economy. They might come in handy when heavy loads carried in the car's trunk would hamper the car's aerodynamic efficiency. The levelers can return the car body to its most efficient position.

**Roof rack.**
If you must have one because you think it gives your car a sporty look, don't use it to carry bulky items. A roof rack might come in handy once a year during your vacation, but it'll increase your car's wind resistance all the time.

**Air deflectors.**
You see these on station wagons. They deflect the air from over the top of the wagon down past the rear window. The idea is to keep the exhaust from being sucked back into the window and keep the rear window free of dirt and snow. They'll rob you of economy simply because they're made to catch the air.

**High-pressure radial tires.**
These are specially designed to make the most of the radial design. Typically, the tires take an inflation of from 32 to 35 pounds per square inch. That makes them harder, less subject to flexing, and able to roll easier than non-radials. The high pressures and hardness call for special compensating features in the car's suspension system. If you use high-pressure radials on an older car that's not set up to handle the harder ride, you'll get a buckboard effect on rough pavement.

*"I'd suggest 20 gallons of gas"*

**Radial tires.**
They provide up to 6 percent better fuel economy than bias tires; they roll more smoothly and last longer, too. On balance, their longer life should make up for their higher initial cost. Most cars built in the past five years were designed to take radials.

**Bias-belted tires.**
A choice of these should be made on the basis of purchase price, not operating costs. The belted feature of this tire is a half-way step between the old-fashioned bias tire and the radial tire. The fuel economy available with bias-belted tires is close to that of the radials, but the former lack the refinements in ride and handling provided by the latter.

**Bias tires.**
These are the bottom of the barrel when it comes to fuel economy and many other characteristics that affect ride, handling, and comfort. Their underlying plies flex against one another each time the tire moves; that causes friction and a resultant increase in fuel consumption. Buy these tires only if you are planning to sell your car soon. They're virtually obsolete.

**Compact spare tires.**
These tires, meant to be used only in emergencies, are not a good idea. They weigh less than conventional spares, but not enough to make a noticeable difference in mileage. Furthermore, the price differential between a compact and a conventional spare is insignificant when spread out over the life of the tire.

**Snow tires.**
Usually, these heavy, aggressively treaded tires do nothing to improve fuel economy. In fact, they are usually second-line designs that are built almost exclusively to improve traction. A good set of radials will nearly duplicate the traction capabilities of most snow tires and will be more economical to run.

**Special wheels.**
These wheels can add up to 25 pounds to the weight of your car. Get lightweight wheel covers instead. They're cheaper and don't weigh more than 10 pounds, yet look just as nifty.

## Air conditioner.

Granted, there are some cars that are difficult to sell used without air conditioning. Buyers of previously owned luxury cars often will reject any car that is not so equipped. But if you think you will keep the car a few years and therefore aren't too worried about problems you might eventually have in reselling it, save the $500 or so that an air conditioner costs as a new-car option. The typical air conditioner in most domestic cars weighs about 100 pounds, so even if you never turn it on it'll cost you about 0.2 mpg wherever you go.

## Dual air conditioners.

Sold mainly for vans and large station wagons of the Chevrolet Suburban type, a dual air conditioning system is a gas gulper. On warm days, a full load of passengers might need the second air conditioner, but its use will be very costly.

## Sunroofs.

They take the place of air conditioning many times, and therefore save energy. They are a good addition to a car's ventilation system, promoting excellent circulation of air inside the car. They do what open windows do, however; they increase a car's drag. And a sunroof, priced at $400 to $500, costs as much as an air conditioning system.

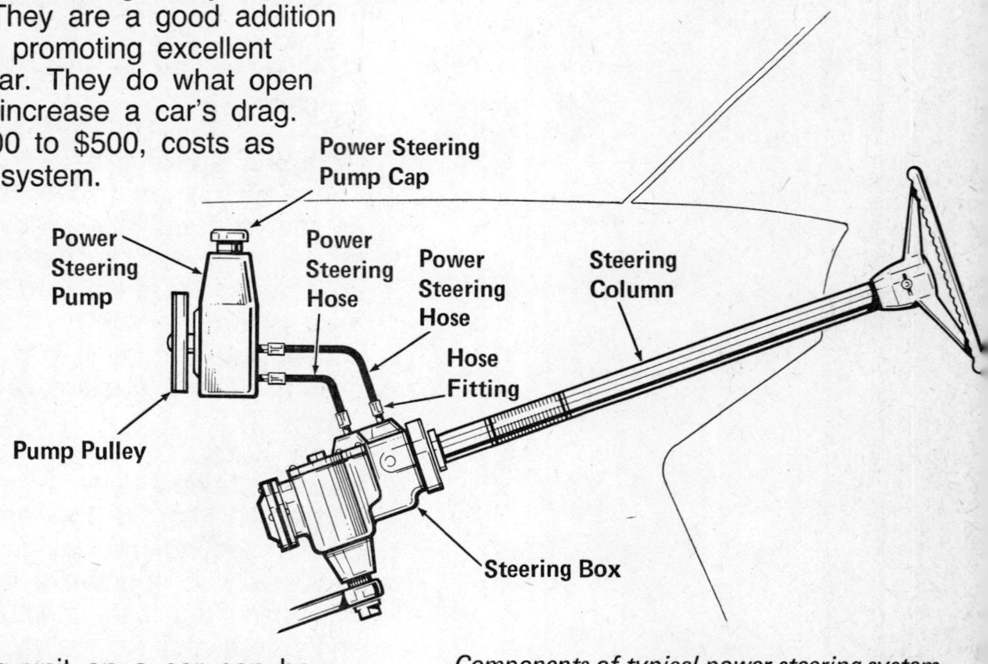


*Components of typical power steering system.*

## Power steering.

The drag of a power steering unit on a car can be considerable, but only intermittently. When the car's wheels are not rolling, maximum effort from the power booster is needed to turn the front wheels (you can hear the engine straining). But power steering is worth the extra cost on bigger cars because of the improvement in control it provides. The energy it takes from the engine is miniscule in most types of driving. Power steering does not deserve deletion from a new-car accessory list.

**Power brakes.**
A couple of techniques are used to power brake assists of cars; neither of them robs you of a measurable amount of fuel. If you like the feel of power brakes, go ahead and buy them.

**Tinted glass.**
This is a necessity for air-conditioned cars, and makes hot weather travel more comfortable in all models. Tinted glass reduces the dependence on air conditioning, and therefore improves fuel economy.

**Speed control.**
Buy only if you do a lot of driving. This option costs about $100 new, and boosts mileage considerably only when used on long, flat stretches of highway. If you do much highway motoring, this can be a good way to save fuel; if you don't, skip this option. Such a device is useless in city traffic.

**Electric fan rear defogger.**
Choose a heated-wire type instead. The electric-fan type draws more electrical current than the wire. (You have to burn fuel to generate electricity.)

**Wire-type window defoggers.**
We recommend them. They are more efficient than the forced-air type. If you want a rear window defogger and didn't buy one when you bought your car, you can buy an aftermarket model. It'll be easy to install and will do an excellent job. Any such high-efficiency device that removes fog or ice from your window is better than using your car's built-in defroster, which requires you to run your engine for many minutes while you wait for the windows to clear.

**Tachometer.**
Sold mostly as a performance gauge, a tachometer can also increase mileage. A tach measures the speed of the engine—a factor in engine efficiency. Order one when you buy a new car; buy an aftermarket tach for your present car.

**MPG gauge.**
On newer, more expensive car models you can get electronic readouts that tell you how many mpgs you're getting at any time. They depend on the car's speedometer for some basic information, and some speedometers are incorrect by as much as 5 mph at 60 mph. So we don't think an mpg gauge will prove worth its cost.

**Rally instruments and trip odometer.**
These items are usually sold as a package and include gauges for oil pressure, coolant temperature, and battery condition in addition to the standard gauges. Some packages include a tachometer too. For the really serious driver who wants to insure that his car is always performing at its best, rally instruments may be the ticket. An odometer can make mileage calculation easy.

**Lamp groups.**
They come in various combinations on different cars. They usually consist of extra lamps in the trunk, at the interior floor, and under the hood, and may include a delay provision to keep the lamps on for a few seconds after the doors are closed or a switch is turned off. They take little energy to run, and for the safety and convenience that is offered to some buyers, they can be real bargains. They have no effect on fuel economy.

**Heavy-duty battery.**
This option might save you gas in starting in cold weather and being able to maintain a good charge at all times. However, why buy more battery than you need, especially if it has little effect on general fuel economy? Skip this unless you have experienced battery problems in the past.

**Heavy-duty alternator.**
This is not needed for most driving conditions. Its value is not related to fuel economy.

**Radio systems.**
The drain on the car's battery caused by radios is negligible. Don't be afraid to purchase exotic equipment here.

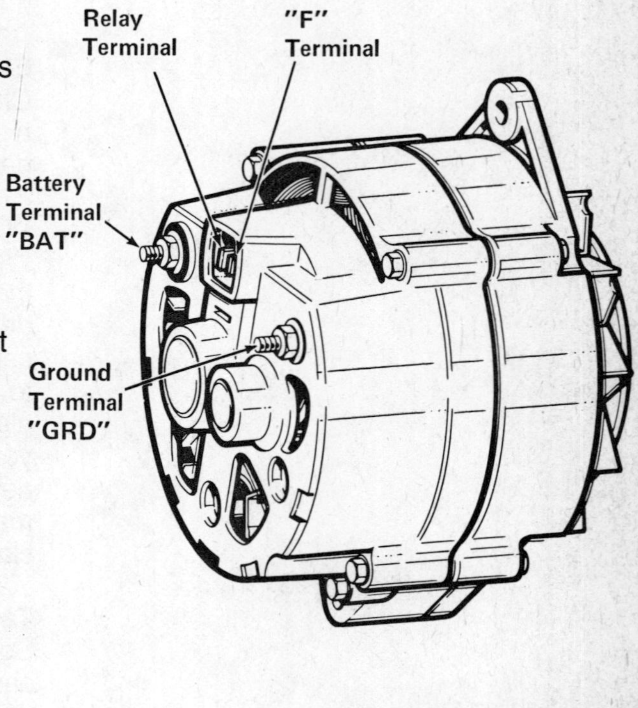


*Rear view of heavy-duty alternator showing connections to battery and electrical system.*

**Vinyl tops.**
They weigh only seven pounds or so, and do not affect fuel economy for that reason. The color is important in controlling interior temperatures. In warm climates, avoid black roofs; select light colors, especially white, which will reflect sunlight and help keep the interior cool. In colder climes, choose a black vinyl roof, which will absorb heat and help to warm up the interior of the car.

**Power Seats.**
These are a real energy drain. They weigh an extra 18-25 pounds, take lots of energy to operate, and generally are useful only when several different people drive the same car.

**Extra wagon seat.**
Think before you order a three-seat wagon or a multiple-seat van. Will the extra seat be worth the extra cost and the extra gasoline required to carry it around? It'll weigh 50 to 100 pounds. Be sure it will be sat on, or else avoid buying it.

**Trailer air deflector.**
Ever notice those rounded sheets of metal attached to the roofs of semitrailer trucks? They're designed to reduce the wind resistance of the trailer. Smaller versions are available for passenger cars that are used to pull travel trailers. The advantage they offer depends on the trailer's shape, so we can't say how greatly they affect mileage. But it's safe to assume that what works for the big trucks will work for your car.

**Avoid aerodynamic aids.**
Add-on devices like rear spoilers and front air dams may look racy, but their benefit to fuel economy is negligible at best. Most of these devices are advertised as reducing air drag and improving stability at high speed. Some are claimed to produce better gas mileage, too. But bolting one of these devices onto your car may actually increase the amount of drag and increase fuel consumption. Most aftermarket devices have not been scientifically tested. They are simply cosmetic add-ons inspired by similar devices used on race cars. At racing speeds a spoiler or air dam is useful and effective; their effectiveness on passenger cars traveling at 55 miles per hour is debatable.

# MILEAGE CHARTS

One of the more effective ways to save gasoline is to keep a record of gasoline use and cost. Here are some charts to make this convenient.

Here's how to use them.

**Column A:** Here's where you put the date of your fill-up.

**Column B:** Enter your odometer reading here as you fill up. This will tell you how many miles you start with. You'll need this figure to determine how many miles you travel on each tank of gas.

**Column C:** The second time you fill up, enter the car's new odometer reading in Column B. Then subtract the previous reading from this figure. Enter the remainder in Column C. For example: If your odometer reading was 2000 miles the first time and 2200 miles the second time, subtract 2000 from 2200 and get a remainder of 200 miles.

**Column D:** Take a guess (or better yet, keep an exact record) as to what portion of your total mileage was traveled on the highway and what portion was traveled in the city. Enter the miles for each type of driving here. For example: If, while putting 200 miles on your car in a week, you traveled 175 miles in the city and 25 miles on the highway, write 175/25 in this space. This will be informative when you calculate your mileage. A lot of city driving will keep your mileage low; a lot of highway driving will raise your mileage.

**Column E:** Here's where you write down the number of gallons you needed to fill your tank. For mileage-calculating purposes, it's wise to fill your tank yourself and try to fill it to the same level every time. If you always stop at the same gas station, you might become familiar with the pump's automatic shutoff and use this to consistently fill your tank to the desired level.

**Column F:** The most important number. To calculate this figure, divide Column C by Column E. For example: You drove a total of 200 miles between your most recent fill-up and the one before that. Your car needed 10 gallons. So you divide 200 miles by 10 gallons and get 20 miles per gallon.

**Column G:** Write down the price of a gallon of gas. This isn't needed for mileage calculation, but you might want to keep track of how rapidly gas prices are increasing in your area.

**Column H:** Multiply Column G by Column E. For example: You filled up with 10 gallons, and gas costs $1.10 a gallon. Multiply 10 by $1.10 and get an answer of $11.

**Column I:** Use this space to keep a record of the tips you use. In this way, you will be able to compare their effectiveness. Did you save more gas this week by always putting your car's transmission into neutral at stoplights than you did last week by not doing so?

We've provided plenty of charts, so you'll be able to maintain a record of your driving habits and gasoline use for many weeks. If you force yourself to keep such a complete record, you're bound to become more aware of how you use gasoline. And that's bound to make you a more efficient driver.

| A<br>Date of Fill-Up | B<br>Odometer Reading | C<br>Total Miles Traveled | D<br>Estimated Miles Traveled City/Highway | E<br>Gallons Needed To Fill Up | F<br>Miles per Gallon | G<br>Cost per Gallon | H<br>Fuel Cost This Period | I<br>Tips Used |
|---|---|---|---|---|---|---|---|---|
| | | | | | | | | |
| | | | | | | | | |
| | | | | | | | | |
| | | | | | | | | |
| | | | | | | | | |
| | | | | | | | | |
| | | | | | | | | |
| | | | | | | | | |
| | | | | | | | | |
| | | | | | | | | |
| | | | | | | | | |

| A<br>Date of Fill-Up | B<br>Odometer Reading | C<br>Total Miles Traveled | D<br>Estimated Miles Traveled City/Highway | E<br>Gallons Needed To Fill Up | F<br>Miles per Gallon | G<br>Cost per Gallon | H<br>Fuel Cost This Period | I<br>Tips Used |
|---|---|---|---|---|---|---|---|---|
| | | | | | | | | |
| | | | | | | | | |
| | | | | | | | | |
| | | | | | | | | |
| | | | | | | | | |
| | | | | | | | | |
| | | | | | | | | |
| | | | | | | | | |
| | | | | | | | | |
| | | | | | | | | |
| | | | | | | | | |

| A<br>Date of Fill-Up | B<br>Odometer Reading | C<br>Total Miles Traveled | D<br>Estimated Miles Traveled City/Highway | E<br>Gallons Needed To Fill Up | F<br>Miles per Gallon | G<br>Cost per Gallon | H<br>Fuel Cost This Period | I<br>Tips Used |
|---|---|---|---|---|---|---|---|---|
| | | | | | | | | |
| | | | | | | | | |
| | | | | | | | | |
| | | | | | | | | |
| | | | | | | | | |
| | | | | | | | | |
| | | | | | | | | |
| | | | | | | | | |
| | | | | | | | | |
| | | | | | | | | |
| | | | | | | | | |

| A<br>Date of Fill-Up | B<br>Odometer Reading | C<br>Total Miles Traveled | D<br>Estimated Miles Traveled City/Highway | E<br>Gallons Needed To Fill Up | F<br>Miles per Gallon | G<br>Cost per Gallon | H<br>Fuel Cost This Period | I<br>Tips Used |
|---|---|---|---|---|---|---|---|---|
| | | | | | | | | |
| | | | | | | | | |
| | | | | | | | | |
| | | | | | | | | |
| | | | | | | | | |
| | | | | | | | | |
| | | | | | | | | |
| | | | | | | | | |
| | | | | | | | | |
| | | | | | | | | |
| | | | | | | | | |